C000257525

the

a natural history

PHIL HOCKEY

WWF

'WWF-SA has identified the African
Penguin as a flagship species for the
conservation of marine biodiversity.'

ROB LITTLE
Director: Conservation

Struik Publishers (Pty) Ltd
(a member of the Struik
New Holland Group (Pty) Ltd)
Cornelis Struik House
80 McKenzie Street
Cape Town, 8001
Reg. No. 1954/000965/07
First edition 2001

10 9 8 7 6 5 4 3 2 1

Publishing Manager: Pippa Parker
Managing Editor: Helen de Villiers
Editors: Peter Joyce, Jeanne Hromnik
Designer: Janice Evans
Design Assistant: Illana Fridkin

Reproduction by Hirt and Carter
Cape (Pty) Ltd
Printed and bound by
Creda Communications (Pty) Ltd,
Cape Town.

ISBN 1 86872 523 5

PHOTOGRAPHIC CREDITS

AF=Albert Froneman; AP=Alain Proust; AW=Anton Wolfaardt; BD=Bruce Dyer; CA=Cape Argus;
CM=Charles Maxwell; CPL=Cape Photo Library; CV=Claudio Velasquez; ET=Erhardt Thiel;
GA=Gallo Images; JBP=J&B Photographers; KP=Kim Prochazka; LU=Lisa Upfold; MCM=Marine
and Coastal Management; ME=Markus Essler; ND=Nigel Dennis; OH=Onno Huyser; PA=Photo
Access; PS=Peter Steyn; PH=Phil Hockey; RC=Rob Crawford; RdlH=Roger de la Harpe; RHP=Rod
Haester Photography; SA=Shaen Adey; SIL=Struik Image Library; SU=Source Unknown; TS=Tony
Stone; TvD=Tony van Dalsen; US=Underwater Services

Cover (CV); Page 1 (AW); 2-3 (PH); 4 (CM/US); 7 (MCM); 8-9 (PH); 10 (BD); 11 (BD); 12 top
(RdlH/SIL), bottom (ME/PA); 13 top (PH), bottom (PS/PA); 14-15 (CM/US); 16 top (AW), bottom
(BD); 17 top (ND/SIL), bottom (PH); 18 both (PH); 19 both (CV); 20 (CV); 21 (KP); 22 (PH);
23 (CM/US); 24-25 (PH); 26 (AW); 27 both (PH); 28 (CM/US); 29 top (BD), bottom (PH); 30 top (PH),
bottom (CV); 31 both (CV); 32-33 (CV); 34 top (BD), bottom (RC); 35 top (CV), bottom (BD);
36 (CV); 37 top (BD), bottom (PH); 38 (BD), top right (SA/SIL); 39 both (BD); 40 top (PH),
bottom (CV); 41 (LU); 42-43 (BD); 44 (MCM); 45 top (AW), bottom (MCM); 46 (SA/SIL); 47 top
(SU), bottom (AW); 48 (KP); 50 (CA); 51 (TvD); 52 all (TvD); 53 both (TvD); 54 (MCM); 55 top
(RHP/PA), bottom (OH); 56-57 (ET/SIL); 58 both (PH); 59 top (PH), bottom (TvD); 60 all on left,
top right (PH); bottom right (BD); 61 (CA); 62 (CPL/AP); 63 both (ND/SIL); 64-65 (AW); 66 top
(ND/SIL), bottom (PH); 67 both (PH); 68 top left and right (PH), bottom (AW); 69 top left (PH),
top right (JBP/PA), bottom left (AF), bottom right (ND/SIL); 70-71 (AW)

ACKNOWLEDGEMENTS

I am grateful to Rob Crawford, Bruce Dyer, Onno Huyser, Peter Joyce, Kim Prochazka,
Peter Ryan, Rory Wilson, Anton Wolfaardt and Phil Whittington for comments on, and
additions to, my original manuscript. Any errors are my responsibility alone.
I also thank Tony van Dalsen for tracking down and scanning historical photographs,
and Charles Maxwell for making digital video images available.

CONTENTS

WALVIS BAY

Hollams Bird Island
Sylvia Hill

NAMIBIA

BOTSWANA

Mercury Island

Ichaboe Island
Halifax Island
LÜDERITZ

SOUTH AFRICA

Possession Island
Pomona Island
Plumpudding Island
Sinclair Island

B
E
N
G
U
E
L
A

C
U
R
R
E
N
T

LES•

Penguin Numbers

○ > 10 000
○ 1000 - 10 000
○ < 1000

LAMBERTS BAY

Bird Island
Marcus Island
Malgas Island
Jutten Island
Vondeling Island
Dassen Island
Robben Island
SALDHANA

EAST LONDON

Algoa Bay

PORT ELIZABETH
Stag Island
Bird Island
Seal Island

Boulders Beach
Seal Island
Stony point
Dyer Island
Geyser Island
CAPE TOWN
BETTY'S BAY
CAPE AGULHAS

Jahleel Island
Brenton Rock
St Croix Island

ATLANTIC
OCEAN

INDIAN
OCEAN

INTRODUCTION

Penguins are fascinating creatures, intriguing scientists and tourists alike. Whether offering us the mystery and beauty of a 300-metre dive or entertaining us with comic clumsiness on land, these charismatic creatures delight the eye and captivate the heart.

Most of the world's penguins inhabit the remote islands of the southern oceans, where only a handful of visitors are privileged enough to see them. However, in South Africa, within 20 km of Cape Town, there is a mainland colony of African Penguins readily accessible to the public; and another two within easy distance, one on the mainland and one on Table Bay's once-notorious Robben Island. The birds of the Boulders colony, near Simon's Town, are well accustomed to the presence of people and provide unsurpassed opportunities for observation and photography. From moulting to mating, bathing to breeding, their daily lives and dramas are played out within a few feet of enthralled visitors.

This book aims to enhance the experience of visual and personal contact with the birds by explaining, among other things, how Africa's penguins are adapted for life at the ocean's edge. It also explores the question of why, despite these adaptations, the number of penguins has fallen by more than 90 per cent during the past hundred years.

AFRICAN PENGUIN
FACT FILE

Common names: ENGLISH: African Penguin, Jackass Penguin (named for its donkey-like braying call), Cape Penguin, Black-footed Penguin.
AFRIKAANS: Brilpikkewyn.
XHOSA: Inguza, Unombombiya.
GERMAN: Haubentaucher.
FRENCH: Manchot du Cap.
PORTUGUESE: Pinguím.

Family: Spheniscidae.

Scientific name: *Spheniscus demersus*. *Spheniscus* is a diminutive of the Greek word *spen*, a 'wedge', referring to the streamlined swimming shape; *demersus* is a Latin word meaning 'plunging'.

Size: height about 50 cm; body weight 2,1–3,7 kg.

Distinguishing adults and juveniles: juveniles are entirely blue-grey above and lack the white face-markings and black breast-band of the adults.

Distinguishing adult males and females: very difficult. Males are larger and have larger bills; these differences can usually be seen only when a pair is together.

World population size: about 179 000 adults, 56 000 breeding pairs.

Breeding range: from Hollams Bird Island, Namibia, to Bird Island, Algoa Bay (E. Cape).

Colonies: 24 on islands, 3 on mainland.

Non-breeding range: regularly moves north and east of the breeding range, especially to coasts of northern Namibia and southern Angola.

Extreme records from Gabon and southern Mozambique.

Breeding season: all year, but mostly March to May in South Africa, November and December in Namibia.

Age at first breeding: 2–6 years, usually 4 years.

Eggs: 1–2, usually 2, white; weight 105 g.

Incubation period: 40 days.

Fledging period: 60–130 days.

Lifespan: average 10–11 years, maximum 24 years.

Swimming speed: up to 15–20 km/h; average 5 km/h when travelling.

Dive depth: usually less than 30 m, but up to a maximum of 130 m.

Dive duration: about 2–5 minutes when feeding; dives are usually shorter during travel.

Food: shoaling fish and squid.

Conservation status: numbers are decreasing by about 2% per year.

International Red Data Book status: Vulnerable.

South African Red Data Book status: Vulnerable.

Main threats from humans:
historical: hunting, guano scraping, egg collecting;
modern: commercial fishing, oil pollution.

Opposite: The spots on the breast and belly are variable and cannot be used to distinguish males and females.

PERSPECTIVE

'*The wonderment of the early mariner was understandable.
No bird of land or air is so extraordinary – or as
closely akin to him in bearing and gait.*'

Mike Holmes, *Cry of the Jackass*, 1976

Nesting penguins at Mercury Island, Namibia.

The African Penguin, the only penguin species to breed in Africa, is confined largely to the cold waters of the extreme southwest, breeding on scattered islands along the South African and southern Namibian coasts.

Its distribution coincides roughly with the Benguela Current, a cool, northward-flowing, nutrient-rich body of water that is forced to the surface by strong winds, especially in summer – a process called upwelling. A large and isolated penguin population in Algoa Bay, on the Eastern Cape coast, also occurs in the vicinity of a localized, nutrient-rich upwelling system.

The distribution of the birds is further determined by the availability of offshore islands as breeding sites.

Five million years ago, the story of the penguin in Africa was very different. Terrestrial habitats along the Benguela coast were not as they are now. The land was much more tropical and where short scrub and small mammals now predominate, a warm tropical woodland was home back then to bears, sabre-toothed cats and the forerunners of modern-day giraffes and elephants. All this changed when the southwestern coast began to develop its Mediterranean climate.

Despite the tropical fauna on land, the marine environment of southern Africa at the time was closer to that of the modern sub-Antarctic, and included birds of the deep south, such as diving petrels, which no longer occur as far north as Africa.

Among the bird fossils that have been discovered in southern Africa are those of no fewer than four species of penguin, all of which are thought to belong to the same genus *Spheniscus* as the modern African Penguin. They all date from the late Miocene period, some five million years ago. The smallest was slightly smaller than the African Penguin; the largest was more than twice its size. When and why these birds became extinct is not known.

Today, the islands of the sub-Antarctic are home to several species of penguin. Even though some of the islands are not far, in global terms, from the African mainland – the Prince Edward Islands are less than 2 000 km away – none of these birds is closely related to the African Penguin. Its nearest relatives are found almost 9 000 km away, along the coast of southern South America. The two species that occur there, the Humboldt Penguin

S. humboldti and the Magellanic Penguin *S. magellanicus* are very similar in size, appearance and behaviour to the African Penguin. Its only other close relative is the world's most tropical penguin, the Galapagos Penguin *S. mendiculus*, which is found only on the Galapagos Islands.

The evolution of penguins is not well understood because the fossil record is very incomplete. The birds are confined to the southern hemisphere, but where and when they first evolved is a mystery. What is certain, however, is that their common ancestor was not a flightless, but a flying, bird.

The earliest 'proto-penguin' bones were discovered in New Zealand and are approximately 55 million years old. This is a much older bird than the four fossil penguin species found in southern Africa. Penguins probably appeared on Earth after the massive extinction of marine reptiles at the end of the Cretaceous

Breeding in burrows – an adaptation to escape the sun's heat.

The first penguins on Earth evolved 55–65 million years ago.

less, which, as it turns out, was to be its undoing. It was hunted to extinction by man in the mid-19th Century, largely because its fat had commercial value. The word 'penguin' derives from the same value – it comes from the Latin word *pinguis*, meaning fat, which is very close to the present day Portuguese *pinguím*.

The fossil record has unveiled no fewer than 32 extinct species of penguin (nearly twice as many as the 17 species that survive today). The Little Penguin *Eudyptule minor* of South Australia and New Zealand is the only living penguin species represented among the fossils. Some fossil penguins were much larger than any living penguins. *Pachydyptes* and *Anthropornis* stood at more than 1,5 m tall, almost the height of a man.

period, about 65 million years ago. This coincided with the great dinosaur extinction, and created opportunities for new life forms to evolve and to fill the niches left by those that had gone.

In the perspective of other marine animals, it is fairly certain that penguins pre-date whales, dolphins and seals. The earliest whales appeared, in the northern hemisphere, 45–50 million years ago, and the earliest fossil dolphins from the southern hemisphere are no more than 30 million years old. There is no evidence that penguins ever occurred in the northern hemisphere, where their place was filled by the auks and puffins.

Although similar in appearance to penguins, auks and puffins have retained the flying abilities of their ancestors, with one exception. The Great Auk *Alca impennis* of the North Atlantic was flight-

Northern hemisphere puffins are not closely related to penguins despite their obvious similarity in appearance.

The Humboldt Penguin of South America is closely related to the African Penguin.

Although we are uncertain of the immediate ancestor of the penguin, recent advances in genetic research have allowed us to identify its closest living relatives. Northern auks and puffins look much like penguins, but they are only very distantly related. The nearest relatives to penguins are two groups of highly accomplished flying birds, frigatebirds and petrels, which have predominantly tropical and southern hemisphere distributions, respectively. The other close relatives, the divers (known as loons in North America), are confined to the northern hemisphere. It seems, therefore, that the evolutionary route to penguins in the south was paralleled by a radiation of divers in the northern hemisphere.

Among penguins, the African Penguin and its close relatives (the Humboldt, Magellanic and Galapagos Penguins) are unusual. Most penguins are found in cold Antarctic and sub-Antarctic places, and they have evolved special adaptations for life in such harsh environments, including highly modified feathers and a layer of subcutaneous fat to provide insulation against the freezing polar seas. Although African Penguins are well suited to life in the cold waters of the Benguela Current, such adaptations work against them when they come ashore to breed in habitats that are much warmer than those used by their more southerly counterparts. How they cope with these warmer conditions is discussed in the chapter entitled 'Life on land'.

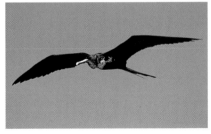

Frigatebirds, masters of the air, are among penguins' closest living relatives.

**ADAPTATIONS
FOR LIFE UNDER WATER**

'The penguin's natural element is the sea. He cannot walk with any elegancy or convenience, nor can he fly; but he can swim almost as swiftly as the shark and the fiercest storm has no terrors for him.'

Cherry Kearton, *Penguin Island*, 1960.

The shape of penguins is almost entirely geared to life in the sea.

L ife in the water and life in the air impose very different design constraints. Flying birds require light bodies and large wing areas, but for birds that 'fly' under water, large wings are a hindrance. Diving ducks, for example, rely almost entirely on their feet for propulsion beneath the surface, keeping their wings tucked in close to the body. However, there is a limit to the speed that can be generated under water by the use of feet alone.

Northern auks do use their wings in water, but to do so they have evolved small ones, which limits them in the air. Some seabirds that are adept under water, notably the diving petrels, have such small wings that the loss of even a few wing feathers renders them flightless.

Soft lenses and specialized eye muscles allow penguins to see adequately both on land and under water.

The clumsy landlubber becomes a sleek underwater predator.

Penguins have taken wing reduction to its evolutionary conclusion. Early in their history they lost the ability to fly, opting rather to perfect their underwater design. Their wings became hard flippers, and the feathers covering them have been miniaturized and waterproofed. Indeed, the entire surface layer of their body feathers has the same properties, the waterproofing provided, in part, by the feather structure. The feathers are hard and stiff, with a flattened shaft, and overlap to provide extra insulation.

The more tropical penguins, such as the African Penguin, have shorter feathers than those of their Antarctic cousins, who face much colder temperatures. Long or short, however, perfectly waterproofed feathers require regular lubrication.

Oil from a gland at the base of the tail is used to waterproof the feathers.

Totally at home in pounding Atlantic surf.

Feet provide some surface propulsion; flippers are used under water.

Situated above the base of the penguin's tail is a gland, called a preen gland, from which the bird transfers oil to its feathers with its bill.

All flying birds, and most flightless ones too, have pneumatized bones. The centres of the long bones are designed like sponges, with many air pockets that are connected to the respiratory system. This arrangement keeps the bird as light as possible. For penguins, however, pneumatized bones would be a disadvantage because they would increase penguins' buoyancy when diving under water. As a result, penguins have lost their pneumatization and have developed heavy, solid bones like those of mammals.

Although flippers provide the propulsion for underwater travel, penguins do use their webbed feet when swimming on the surface. This is a slow way for the birds to travel and they can move at only about 1,5 km/h, as against the speed of 6–8 km/h that they can easily achieve under water. As soon as they dip below the surface, propulsion comes from the flippers, and they use their feet (and heads) primarily as rudders.

African Penguins remain on land for almost three weeks when moulting.

CHANGING FEATHERS

Although body and feather design has been carried to extremes by the African Penguin, its feathers, like those of other birds, become worn in time. Like all birds, penguins have to moult, usually once or twice a year. In South Africa, most moult between November and January, before the breeding peak; in Namibia, most moult in April and May.

Penguins can swim faster with new feathers than with old. However, moulting puts a sudden halt to their aquatic lifestyle; their waterproofing is lost and their ability to swim under water is greatly reduced. Indeed, insulation and hunting ability are so badly impaired during moult that penguins are forced to remain on land.

If penguins took months to complete one moult, or years like some species of birds, they would starve to death. To speed up their moult, they have evolved a unique and ingenious method: prior to moulting, they remain at sea and lay down fat deposits in the way other birds do prior to migration. African Penguins take about five weeks to fatten at sea, eating almost 1,2 kg of fish per day and increasing the weight of their bodies by about 30 per cent.

At the same time, their new feathers start to develop under the skin. Once their fat deposits are sufficiently large, the penguins come ashore and immediately start shedding their old feathers. Stranded on land, they lose weight at the rate of about 90 g per day. Even though the entire moult is completed in only 19–20 days, a moulting bird can lose almost half its body weight during the process.

At the end of the moult, a somewhat slimmer, but very sleek, penguin returns to the sea, where it will spend about six weeks fattening up again. When they are moulting on land, African Penguins look very puffy and untidy. People sometimes mistake moulters for sick birds; they are not sick – though perhaps a bit hungry. Because moulting birds are on an extremely tight energy budget, it is important that they be disturbed as little as possible.

Other species of penguin also undergo rapid moults. The African Penguin's close relative in the Galapagos Islands completes its moult in only 12–13 days, and even the world's largest penguin, the mighty 30-kg Emperor Penguin *Aptenodytes forsteri* stays ashore for only 34 days.

This penguin will lose almost half its body weight by the end of its moult.

PENGUINS AT SEA: THE CHALLENGE

Many of the most interesting facets of a penguin's life are hidden from human view below the sea's surface – a particular challenge for scientists because they cannot observe the birds in natural conditions in their true element.

However, ingenious applications of modern technology have uncovered many penguin secrets in recent times. It was less than 20 years ago that we first discovered just how deep African Penguins dive. The breakthrough was achieved using a clever modification of an ordinary diver's depth gauge in the form of a capillary tube in which the position of the water meniscus (the water's 'skin', created by surface tension) is determined by the outside water pressure, hence by the depth.

A tiny bead of wax containing radioactive phosphorus was placed on the meniscus. The capillary tube itself was attached to a small sheet of radiation-sensitive film encased in a black plastic sachet, and the entire wafer-thin device was strapped to the back of a penguin with a simple neoprene harness.

By attaching the device to one of a breeding pair, researchers could be certain of recovering the device when the penguin next returned to the nest. Every time the penguin dived at sea, the meniscus, and hence the radioactive bead, would move in proportion to the depth of the diving bird, and the intensity of the radiation would be proportional to the time the bird spent at each depth. This created a trace on the film that could be developed to provide a record of the time the penguin spent at different depths.

Although this device is ingenious and its results revealing, it is primitive in the extreme when compared with the remote recording equipment that has been developed recently.

Modern devices, designed in Germany and tested in South Africa, can track the movements of a swimming penguin in real time, and there is even one that can simultaneously measure speed, direction (in three dimensions), depth, light levels and water temperature.

This allows the penguin's entire day at sea to be mapped. An additional simple implant will also record when a hunting dive is successful and how many fish are eaten. Hand-made phosphorus beads and plastic capillary tubes have been replaced by sophisticated microprocessors and miniaturized compasses. The products of Silicon Valley are now used all around the world to chart the daily lives of marine birds.

For scientists, studying penguins at sea is a technological challenge.

Surface travel is slow because flippers cannot be used to their full advantage.

Underwater swimming is not only faster but also more energy-efficient than swimming on the surface because less turbulence is created. Even when commuting between the breeding colony and the feeding grounds, penguins prefer to swim under water. It is claimed that penguins are 30 per cent more efficient under water than the best submarines produced by the world's engineers.

Travel under water at high speed requires modification not only of the wings, but of the whole body. Penguins' bodies are superbly streamlined, with the bill flattened to slice through the water. The head, neck and foreparts gradually widen, which minimizes drag.

Moreover, a penguin's eyes are positioned on the side rather than the front of its head. This reduces binocular sight but provides all-round vision, an advantage not only in locating fish prey, but in avoiding predators such as sharks and seals. Special adaptations of the eye muscles coupled with a soft eye-lens, allow the eyes to focus clearly both in and out of the water – something humans cannot do.

Like other birds, penguins must drink. And because they lead an entirely maritime existence, they must drink salt water. To avoid a build-up of salts in their bodies, they have evolved salt glands adjacent to the skull that act as miniature desalination plants, extracting salt out of seawater. The concentrate is expelled through their nostrils. When the birds are on land for extended periods, a ring of white salt crystals begins to build up around their nostrils. Other seabirds, and some birds that live in environments where fresh water is scarce, have the same adaptation.

Feather maintenance is a priority between trips to sea.

When on the hunt for prey, African Penguins can reach a top speed in water approaching 20 km/h. However, this is way above their normal swimming speed. Because African Penguins are flightless and because most of them return daily to feed their young, the distance they can travel away from the breeding colony is limited.

Nonetheless, their potential hunting area is large because of their ability to dive, thereby adding depth to surface range. The average dive lasts about two and a half minutes and regularly takes them down to around 30 m. Their swimming speeds, diving depths and dive times are very similar to those of the Magellanic Penguin and the Humboldt Penguin of South America.

Penguins have paid a price for their perfect adaptation to water: their bodies are poorly designed for moving on land. The comical waddling gait of the birds ashore is in stark contrast to their grace and agility in water.

However, longer, more elegant legs that would help them to move better on land would be a great disadvantage in water. In an evolutionary sense, the costs of being slow and awkward on land are far outweighed by the benefits of being perfectly shaped for life in the water.

DIVING PROBLEMS

When diving, a penguin has to overcome its own buoyancy. Not only is its respiratory system full of air, but more air is trapped beneath its feathers. Combined, this amounts to the buoyancy of a 1,2-litre balloon. The effects of buoyancy are greatest close to the water surface, decreasing with depth as pressure increases. Thus, at a depth of 30 m, the upward lift that the birds have to counteract is only about one-quarter of that close to the surface, which means that the deeper a penguin dives, the faster it is able to swim. By the same token, when a penguin returns from depth to the surface, the lift supplied by the trapped air increases and the rising bird can swim faster and faster. However, research suggests that they maintain a fairly constant speed during a dive, regardless of depth. This implies that the extra energy they expend on the journey down is balanced by energy savings on the way up.

African Penguins regularly swallow stones, and some people mistakenly believe that they do so to counter their buoyancy. The real reason is that the stones help them to grind up their food and thus aid digestion.

Overcoming buoyancy is a problem for diving animals that breathe air through their lungs.

FOOD AND FEEDING

'Very little is known about the techniques used by penguins in prey capture . . . It is not known how penguins locate prey in the darkness, at great depths or at night . . . '

Isabel Martínez, *Handbook of the Birds of the World*, Vol. 1, 1992.

African Penguins head for the fishing grounds in groups . . .

The African Penguin's favoured food is pelagic, shoaling fish such as pilchards (sardines), anchovies, horse mackerel and round herrings, ranging in length from about 10 mm to an extreme of 310 mm. Schools of these small fish roam the ocean, and the penguins must locate a shoal each time they go to sea and, on occasion, each time they dive. They also eat squid, but these are not high-quality food. Squid take longer to digest than fish, and chicks that are fed on squid do not grow as fast as those that receive fish. The African Penguin swallows most of its prey under water, but the larger fish have to be brought to the surface.

Because they cannot fly, African Penguins at sea travel about ten times more slowly than flying seabirds such as gannets and albatrosses. However, they dive to greater depths than other seabird species that feed on the same types of food and in the same areas. Thus, although they may not be able to travel as far out to sea as some other species, they do have a feeding area in deep water that is entirely their own, and in this way avoid competing with other species for food.

The distance the penguins have to travel to find food varies. On the west coast, foraging birds typically cover from 30–70 km on a single trip; on the southern and southeastern coast, at Algoa Bay, foraging trips average 110 km, though they can be as long as 170 km.

However, some west coast African Penguins travel much further. On one trip, a breeding bird from Dassen Island (fitted with a satellite transmitter) made an overnight stop at the Boulders colony near Simon's Town, which must have involved a journey of at least 270 km.

... when they reach the fishing grounds they will separate or split into smaller hunting groups ...

Travelling distance determines the duration of a single foray for food. For west coast birds, this is usually about 10 hours. Birds on the southeast coast were once recorded at sea for as long as 170 hours. Generally, when adults are feeding chicks, the forays become longer and longer as the chicks grow and require ever-increasing quantities of food.

Not only do those birds that are feeding large chicks spend longer at sea; they spend more of their sea time under water.

... returning from a foray, they sprint for the beach to evade marine predators around the colony.

Striped, black-and-white coloration helps confuse shoals of small fish.

A bird feeding small chicks may spend only 30 per cent of its time at sea under water, but this can increase to 90 per cent as the chicks begin to grow.

A single foraging trip is divided into three parts: the journey to and from the fishing grounds, the search for fish, and then the hunt. Because swimming at the surface of the water is slow and inefficient (as described earlier), the normal travelling mode is a series of shallow dives, not more than 3 m below the surface. Each dive lasts about 20 seconds, and the dives are interspersed with 20-second 'breathers'. During these shallow dives, the birds travel along at 6–8 km/h.

They do, however, have the faster option of 'porpoising', which involves shallow, high-speed dives lasting about 14 seconds, after which they propel themselves into the air (like porpoises) for a breathing leap that lasts about a second.

African Penguins travelling in this way can maintain speeds of about 12 km/h, with a top speed of about 19 km/h, but this is very tiring for them. Consequently, penguins normally porpoise only when they are trying to escape from predators such as seals and Killer Whales *Orcinus orca* or when they are following schools of rapidly moving fish.

When they travel to the feeding grounds, penguins usually set off in groups comprising as many as 60 birds. Because they rely on sight to find and catch their prey, they can feed only during daylight hours.

On the west coast, some groups leave the colony early in the morning. Others leave late in the evening, often soon after dark, and make their way in leisurely fashion to the feeding grounds, ready to start hunting at daybreak. When they reach their destination, they separate from each other or split up into small groups of five or fewer birds, and start searching for food in a series of increasingly deep dives. Most dives are less than 30 m deep, although an African Penguin will sometimes dive as deep as 130 m. The Emperor Penguin of Antarctica can dive to more than twice this depth.

Because the eyes of African Penguins are located on the sides of their heads, they can search large areas of water when looking for fish: a penguin below the surface can scan about 170 cubic metres of water per second. On the west coast, the fish they are hunting are usually found in fairly small shoals and, on average, African Penguins spend about two and a half minutes under water on each dive – a short time relative to the Emperor Penguin's 15-minute average!

When hunting under water, penguins have to balance the benefits of a long dive time (more fish caught per dive) against the costs of a long recovery time at the surface. The shorter the dive the shorter

Dull-coloured youngsters rely on stealth to catch their prey.

the recovery. On the south coast, shoaling fish often occur in large aggregations that attract many other predators, some of which, like the Cape Gannet *Morus capensis*, are highly conspicuous. It is thought that penguin dives on the south coast are shorter than in the west because the penguins are able to use other, more mobile. birds to mark the position of the fish. On the west coast they stay down for longer because the risk of losing the fish shoal after they surface is greater.

On average, an adult African Penguin needs about 300 g of fish per day, or 110 kg per year. In total, excluding the extra food needed for rearing their young, the entire African Penguin population consumes about 19 600 tonnes of fish per year. This means that at the beginning of

Breathing time at the surface depends on the length of a dive.

White markings on the heads of some juveniles may help reduce aggression from adults.

the 20th Century, the penguins on Dassen Island alone would have eaten over 150 000 tonnes of fish each year!

Young penguins do not have the black and white patterning of their parents, nor do they hunt the same food. Their meal is more often a slow-moving fish larva than a fast-moving fish. Their dull blue-grey coloration may act as camouflage when they approach prey and may also make them less conspicuous to predators such as sharks and seals.

One thing that juvenile plumage does not do, however, is endear the youngsters to the grown-ups, and they are not often allowed to join hunting parties. However, some juveniles appear to have developed a clever solution: when they moult for the first time, their body colour may still be like that of a young bird, but their new head pattern resembles that of an adult. When they are swimming on the surface, this little piece of deception may be enough for adults to accept them into the hunting group.

Intriguing as this story is, some juveniles with grey heads do manage to atttach themselves to adult hunting parties – clearly an enigma that requires more research.

Even at sea, time is taken out for plumage care.

THE HUNT

When hunting in small groups, Áfrican Penguins co-operate in catching prey. Group members all dive at the same time, and when they locate a shoal, they swim round and round it, forcing the fish to come ever closer together.

Anyone who has watched shoals of fish swimming under water, or in an aquarium, will have noticed how they move in extraordinary synchrony with one another, all changing direction at the same time. What the hunting penguins are trying to do is change the swimming behaviour of the fish from synchronized to chaotic. Chaos is created when the fishes are too close to one another to swim in synchrony, and this is the moment when the penguins strike! They dive beneath the shoal and then attack from below. There are two advantages to this tactic: the penguins are rising from the dark depths, which may make it difficult for fish to see them, and the fish that the birds are chasing are clearly outlined against the light backdrop of the sky.

When an African Penguin grabs a fish, it does so just behind the gill covers. If you have ever been bitten by a penguin, you will know that the specialized shape of the bill allows it to exert enormous pressure, quite enough to puncture human skin. The high-pressure grip probably kills the fish rapidly by compressing both the heart and the gills. The

Backward-pointing barbs on the penguin's tongue and palate help slippery fish on their way down its throat.

captured fish is then swallowed head first, helped on its way down the penguin's throat by rows of backward-pointing barbs on the bird's tongue and palate.

The coloration of the penguins is probably important in causing the initial chaos among the fish. When artificial penguins, painted in different colours, were introduced into aquaria containing pelagic fish, the black and white birds caused much more consternation than did, for example, plain grey birds. It is interesting that Killer Whales and several species of fish-eating dolphins have also

evolved black-and-white striped coloration, presumably to similar ends.

Penguins' black and white coloration may also help them to avoid aquatic predators. By breaking up the outline of the bird, this patterning may make it more difficult for a predator to judge the size of its potential snack.

When these birds dive to hunt, they will all submerge together.

LIFE ON LAND:
THE BREEDING SEASON

'Except for the few patches of bare rock, the whole surface of the island is pitted with holes a few feet apart or less - the nesting burrows of penguins.'

Cherry Kearton, *Penguin Island*, 1960.

Penguins regularly climb steep slopes in search of the best nest sites.

Although African Penguins are beautifully adapted for life in the sea, they must, like all seabirds, come ashore to breed. They are clumsy and ungainly on firm ground, tripping over stones and plants and looking comically out of place.

African Penguins breed in colonies, nesting either in burrows that they excavate themselves or in depressions under large boulders or bushes. A key reason for this choice of nest sites is the need for shade. Hidden nests also provide protection from predators of eggs and chicks, such as gulls.

Although their blubber layer may be an advantage when hunting in cold water, it is a considerable drawback when the penguins are out in the open on a hot African day. It is important to choose the

Mining of guano has prevented many penguins from burrow-nesting.

the AFRICAN **PENGUIN**

right nest site, and the birds go about the process with care. Awkward as they are on land, some select sites more than a kilometre from the sea and as much as half a kilometre up on steep, rocky slopes.

Unlike many other bird species, African Penguins have an extended breeding season. In most colonies, it is possible to find birds at one or another stage of breeding almost throughout the year. In South Africa, the peak of the breeding season (March to May) is later than the peak of the season in Namibia (November and December).

When breeding is about to start, the males come ashore, followed by the females about four days later. Generally, the same pair returns to the same colony, and often to the same nest site, year after year. About 80–90 per cent of pairs remain together for more than one breeding season, and some are known to have been faithful to each other for more than 10 years. When 'divorce' or a change in nest site does occur, it usually follows a failed breeding attempt in an area where nest sites are not in short supply.

Sheltered nest sites provide protection from sun and from aerial predators of eggs and chicks.

Bodies designed for underwater speed make mating a clumsy affair.

Once both members of the pair are ashore, they reinforce their bond and set to work preparing the nest. Mating occurs on land and is a very ungainly procedure, with the male balancing precariously atop the prostrate female. Early in the breeding season, the colony reverberates at night with the braying calls of displaying males – the sound that explains the African Penguin's other name, Jackass Penguin.

About three weeks after the pair returns to the colony, the female lays her eggs. There are usually two eggs, though sometimes only one. These are large, rounded and, when fresh, plain white. It does not take long, however, before they become stained from contact with the ground. By the time the eggs hatch, they have usually turned dirty brown or a shade of green.

Incubation lasts about 40 days, and the male and female participate equally. When one bird is incubating, the other is at sea, feeding. A typical incubation shift lasts about two and a half days. There is a record, however, of one bird incubating continuously for 11 days while it waited for its mate to return from the sea.

Mates may have been separated at sea for several months and must re-establish their bond when they return to breed.

Visitors to penguin colonies often remark on the strange 'head-turning' behaviour of incubating adults in which a bird appears to be eyeing the observer first out of one eye and then out of the other. Quaint and cute as this may appear, it is in fact a threat display, warning you that you are too close to the nest.

Pairs regularly lose their eggs to flooding or predators. In about 30 per cent of cases they will lay replacement eggs. The frequency with which lost clutches are replaced varies from place to place. On Robben Island, even second clutches are rare, whereas pairs in Algoa Bay have been recorded laying as many as four clutches in succession.

The two eggs that are usually laid in a clutch appear about two days apart, but the adults start incubating soon after the first is laid. A consequence of this is that the two chicks also hatch one to two days apart from each other.

In about 90 per cent of successful breeding attempts, only one chick survives to independence. The hatchlings are fluffy and grey, blind and helpless. Once again, the adults share the workload, male and female being equally involved in baby-minding and feeding the young.

Some seabirds, such as terns, that catch food close to their breeding sites, carry food items to their young one at a time. For penguins, this is a poor option as they cannot reach their feeding grounds rapidly. Instead, they transport food back to the colony in bulk in their stomachs – a technique that is used by many other seabirds. including gannets, cormorants, albatrosses, petrels and shearwaters. Penguins are able to slow down their digestion while they are carrying food so that they can give more of it to the chicks.

The chicks are fed by regurgitation, the adult being encouraged to disgorge by the chick's calling and pecking at the base of its parent's bill and around its throat. Since every morsel of food is so precious, the chick pushes its bill down

Preening one another is one way of cementing a partnership.

Dense bushes, as at Boulders, provide shelter for breeding penguins.

the adult's throat to prevent spillage. Not only does this look uncomfortable, but it can be very messy! Unlike their parents, the chicks do not bathe in the sea, so the old food often becomes encrusted around their bills. Anyone who has been bitten by a penguin chick knows that if the skin is broken there is a good chance that the cut will become infected.

Young chicks have to be fed, guarded and kept warm and, for the first 15 or so days after hatching, one parent always broods the young. By then the chicks will have full control over their body temperature but are still at risk from predators, such as gulls, and from the elements, especially rain. Collapsed and flooded burrows are the main cause of death among young chicks.

The braying call of males has given the African Penguin its alternative name, Jackass Penguin.

Young chicks are helpless and require constant attention from their parents.

Growing chicks require ever-increasing amounts of food.

Older chicks sometimes join up in crèches for protection and warmth.

Most parents will be unable to provide enough food for two chicks.

The constant parental vigil continues until the chicks are about 30 days old. At this stage, both parents can go to sea at the same time. When the chicks are left alone, youngsters from several broods sometimes join up and huddle together for protection and warmth. These crèches form most often when chicks are shedding their downy coats and growing their first set of feathers.

The biggest threat to these older chicks is not flooded burrows, but the likelihood of insufficient food. A six-week-old chick requires something like half a kilogram of fish a day! When the young are fully feathered and able to leave the nest they are said to be 'fledged'. The time taken to reach this point can vary greatly, depending on the availability of food and how much the parents were able to provide for the chicks' growth.

Fast-growing chicks can fledge in as little as 60 days; those that have had a leaner time may take as long as 130 days. Body condition also varies at fledging – skinny chicks can weigh as little as 2 kg, fat ones as much as 4 kg. To reach a weight of 4 kg, a chick would have to consume around 25–30 kg of fish.

About 20 per cent of pairs that have successfully reared one brood will immediately start breeding again – sometimes successfully. In years when food is scarce, for instance during the warming of the seas caused by El Niño weather

Extreme colour variants, such as this near-albino, may have little chance of finding a mate.

Feeding their chicks by regurgitation allows parents to bring back large food parcels.

Only half of all youngsters who leave will make it back home.

conditions, breeding failure is common. In 1982/83, shortage of food caused three separate waves of nest desertion at St Croix Island, Algoa Bay. In South America and the Galapagos Islands, penguins may cease breeding altogether during such oceanic anomalies.

African Penguins continue to feed their offspring for as long as the young remain in the colony. When the young leave, they do so alone, unaccompanied by their parents. At this time, their plumage bears little resemblance to that of the adults, being predominantly blue-grey with a whitish belly. These young, inexperienced 'baby blues' heading out to sea for the first time face the most dangerous time of their lives. Only half of all youngsters entering the water on their inaugural swim will make it back home.

The juvenile plumage is retained for 12–22 months, after which the young penguins come ashore for their first moult. Some of these young birds may have been at sea continuously for more than 18 months before returning to land, remaining out for so long that patches of seaweed have grown on their backs and they stagger around on shore like land-lubbers who have spent too long in a boat! Nevertheless, when this first moult is finished, they head back to the water for another trip lasting several months.

The wanderings of juvenile African Penguins take them far from home. Most youngsters from the south coast colonies travel west, and those from west coast colonies move north. Some have been sighted more than 1 000 km away from their birthplaces. The adults, by contrast, even when not breeding, seldom wander more than 400 km from home.

As the youngsters grow older, their visits to the colony become increasingly frequent and, eventually, when they are between two and six years of age, they will be ready to breed for the first time. Most seem to do so at the age of four, though the youngest breeder on record was merely a year and eight months old.

These first-timers do not always return to their home colony to breed, some moving to new colonies if feeding conditions are better there. If they do 'adopt' a new colony, they are likely to breed at this new site for life.

'Baby blues' do not resemble their black and white parents.

STUDYING PENGUINS ON LAND

Almost all the information we have on penguins regarding lifespan, mate choice and movement has come from studies using metal flipper bands.

Because penguins have such short legs, conventional bird rings are of little use in tracking them. Instead, a metal band is placed around the base of the flipper. Each band carries a unique letter and number code and, because the bands are fairly large, these codes can be read in the field.

Researchers sometimes need more detailed information, such as the quantity of food adults bring back to their chicks. An ingenious system has been set up on Robben Island whereby penguins can supply this kind of data without researchers being present! Some of the birds have microchip implants (similar to those carried by long distance runners), each chip emitting a unique signal. As the penguins move to and from the sea, they walk across a hidden balance, which automatically records the bird's weight. A microchip reader identifies the individual.

The difference in a bird's weight between the time it leaves on a foraging trip and its return is a good indicator of how much food the chicks will receive. Among other things, this enables scientists to relate the quantity of food chicks receive to their growth and survival.

By the end of the year 2000, approximately 73 000 African Penguins had been fitted with flipper bands.

POPULATION:
HISTORY, TRENDS
AND THREATS

'Flightless birds have a hard time in the ruthless world of nature, and I suppose that it is for this reason that the penguin is following the Great Auk and the Dodo.'

Lawrence G. Green, *At Daybreak for the Isles*, 1950.

When its existence first became known to the western world, more than five hundred years ago, the African Penguin was a common species. Doubtless the coastal Khoisan of southern Africa already knew of its presence, but it is unlikely that they were ever able to reach the island breeding colonies.

All this changed with the visit of Bartholemeu Diaz and his crew to the Cape in 1487 to 1488. Africa's penguin became the first of the world's penguins to be discovered by Europeans and, undoubtedly, the first penguin to be eaten by westerners.

The earliest surviving written reference to penguins in southern Africa dates from a decade later, after the visit of Vasco da Gama to the Cape in 1497. In the following centuries, seafarers regularly visited the southern African islands, where the huge populations of seabirds provided a ready source of meat and eggs for their ships' larders. Although the flesh of penguins is not pleasant to eat, the eggs were considered a delicacy and the carcasses of birds were rendered down both for fat and as fuel for ships' boilers.

Although it was 'discovered' in the 15th Century, the African Penguin was officially named for science only in 1758, by the Swedish botanist and physician Carolus Linnaeus (1707-1778). Linnaeus was obviously a little confused by the bird, as he placed it in the same genus, *Diomedea,* as the Wandering Albatross.

Unfortunately, there are no reliable estimates of African Penguin numbers at the end of the 19th Century. In the early 1840s, however, something happened that had a major impact on the penguin population, with repercussions that have

Watched by the island's inhabitants, a rowing boat comes ashore at Halifax Island, Namibia (ca. 1900) bringing in guano collectors to scrape away the 'white gold'.

African Penguins have shared many islands with man since European colonization in the 17th Century – to the detriment of the penguins.

lasted well into the present. The South American guano rush, which had started shortly before on the seabird islands off the coast of Peru, spread to Africa. This 'white gold' – seabird droppings – can be transformed into a nutrient-rich agricultural fertilizer (long used as such by the Incas), and literally mountains of accumulated guano were stripped, leaving bare rock behind.

Shanty towns sprang up on the islands off the southern African coast and the accumulation of guano from tens of thousands of years was removed in a matter of months. Although guano scraping continued on some of South Africa's islands right up until 1991, and continues in Namibia even today, it was the initial harvests that had the biggest impact on the penguins.

At Namibia's Ichaboe Island, where 23 m of guano had accumulated, up to 400 ships were anchored around the six-hectare island at the height of the guano rush in 1844, with a British warship in attendance to keep the peace. In all, about 200 000 tonnes of guano were removed.

Stripping of the 23-m guano cap at Ichaboe Island, Namibia, dramatically altered the penguins' breeding environment.

After Ichaboe, the guano collectors' attention shifted south to Malgas Island in Saldanha Bay. Here, a structure was built that allowed 100 boats to load simultaneously. The island was divided up into concessions, and, in 1845, licences were issued to no fewer than 135 vessels. In a few months, the 10-m guano cap was systematically destroyed.

The islands' guano caps had provided a perfect nesting habitat for African Penguins. Because the guano was fairly soft, the birds could excavate nesting burrows sheltered from the heat of the African sun. Insulated below the surface, the nests enjoyed constant cool temperatures. Even when it rained, these burrows served their purpose well because the guano cap acted as an enormous sponge, soaking up the moisture without flooding the nests inside it.

When the guano was removed, those penguins that could not find nest sites under boulders were forced to nest in the open on the rocky island surface, where they were fully at the mercy of the elements and of predators.

Many penguins had to nest on the surface, at the mercy of predators and of the weather, because of the wholesale removal of guano.

Guano harvesting took a terrible toll. Nests in rocky depressions flood easily, drowning eggs and causing young chicks to die of hypothermia. On hot days, adults incubating in the open are unable to keep cool and have to leave their nests to go down to the sea. As soon as eggs and small chicks are left unattended on the surface, they too can either overheat and die or, more likely, fall prey to the ever-watchful Kelp Gulls *Larus dominicanus* and other predators such as the Sacred Ibis *Threskiornis aethiopicus*.

Fifty years on, the guano rush was long past and the islands had been totally transformed, many of them into habitats of poor quality for penguins. Then, at the dawn of the 20th Century, another scourge swept across the penguins' world – egg collecting. This was not the removal of a few eggs to satisfy the desires of museums or private collectors, but wholesale commercial collection for food. Initially, eggs were gathered as a cheap source of protein for the poor. Over time, and with increasing scarcity, they became a luxury food.

No penguin eggs have been collected commercially since 1968, but even before the practice ceased, the African Penguin was faced with another threat – the west-coast 'fish boom' of the post-war years, which targetted the enormous shoals of pilchards. After the stocks of fish collapsed from over-fishing (by the early 1960s), attention shifted to the smaller anchovy. As a result of the depletion of their food supplies, the African Penguin population between Table Bay and Lüderitz (southern Namibia) crashed.

Naturalist Cherry Kearton and friends on Dassen Island in 1931 . . .

THE RAPE OF DASSEN ISLAND

Dassen Island, some 50 km north of Cape Town, is only one of several islands on which penguin eggs were once collected for commercial purposes, but its story is well documented and serves as a good illustration of the magnitude of the pillage.

At the end of the 19th Century, it is estimated that the island was home to 1 400 000 penguins. In the first half of the 20th Century, approximately a half of all eggs laid on the island are reckoned to have been removed by collectors. Between 1900 and 1930, 13 million eggs were collected. In 1919 alone, the harvest totalled 600 000; the average annual harvest from 1917 to 1931 was 460 000 eggs.

If every breeding pair of African Penguins alive in the world today laid 2 eggs, this would still total only 112 000 eggs and be equivalent to just 20 per cent of the 1919 egg harvest on Dassen Island. Even as recently as 1956, 126 800 eggs were collected there, indicating that, only 45 years ago, the African Penguin population on this one island was larger than the entire population of breeding pairs today. Fewer than 17 000 breeding pairs remain on Dassen Island – less than 5 per cent of the numbers a hundred years ago.

. . . and Dassen Island today.

PENGUIN NUMBERS

- At the start of the 20th Century, it is likely that there were more than 2 000 000 African Penguins.
- By the mid-1950s, fewer than 300 000 African Penguins remained – representing a decrease of more than 80 per cent in 50 years.
- By late 1976, numbers had fallen to 222 000, and, by 1986, to just 194 000 birds.
- At present, the total population stands at 179 000 adults, including about 56 000 breeding pairs.

In the course of the 20th Century, 10 colonies were abandoned, but at least 2 of the 3 existing mainland colonies (at Stony Point, Boulders Beach and Sylvia Hill, see page 63) have established themselves in the past two decades. There are now 27 colonies, 24 of which are on off-shore islands.

Simple mathematics predicts that if the penguin population continues to decrease at the same rate, there will be no African Penguins left in the wild 70 years from now. This, however, is an unrealistic prediction because the number of penguins in some colonies is increasing despite the overall pattern of decline. Penguin numbers have stabilized in Algoa Bay and are increasing on Robben Island and at Boulders Beach.

Currently, the two main areas of concern are the islands off the coast of southern Namibia, and Dyer Island, west of Cape Agulhas. On five islands in southern Namibia, numbers of breeding pairs of African Penguins fell by about 75 per cent, from 3 500 pairs in the late 1970s to only 850 pairs by the early 1990s. In the same period, numbers at Dyer Island fell by 60 per cent, from 22 650 pairs to just 8 350 pairs, and since then to below 3 000 pairs: in total, a decrease of more than 85 per cent in 25 years in six island colonies.

Despite a massive decrease in the total number of African Penguins in the past hundred years, numbers at two colonies near Cape Town are on the increase.

On the Namibian island of Possession, the number of breeding pairs fell from 23 000 in 1956 to fewer than 500 in 1987. This decrease is almost exactly what would be predicted for a colony that produced no chicks.

Fortunately, African Penguins rarely become entangled in commercial fishing nets, mainly because the fishing boats hunt at night and the penguins by day. They do, however, like many other sea- and shorebirds, often become entangled in abandoned fishing line – a slow and painful way to die.

Oil pollution is an ever-present threat to seabirds world-wide, especially where large numbers of birds occur close to shipping lanes or major ports. The four most serious oil spills between 1968 and 1994 oiled at least 17 000 African Penguins, which is almost 10 per cent of the present population.

Oiling can kill penguins very quickly. A healthy penguin is well suited to life in cold water, but once it is contaminated with oil it loses much of its insulation. Even at water temperatures as high as 20°C, African Penguins can become hypothermic and, if not rescued, soon die. Oiled penguins tend to head for land and, in trying to preen themselves, swallow the toxic pollutant. Ingestion of oil causes ulceration of soft tissues and the rupturing of red blood cells. If the birds remain on land for too long, they also face the risk of dehydration.

The southern African coast lies along one of the world's major shipping routes and is therefore at high risk from oil pollution. Because African Penguins are concentrated in colonies and are flightless, a single oil spill may have a devastating effect. When the *Kapodistrias* ran aground at Cape Recife, in Algoa Bay, in August 1985, 923 oiled penguins were sent to the SANCCOB (South African Foundation for the Conservation of Coastal Birds) seabird rescue and rehabilitation centre in Cape Town.

Between 1981 and 1991, SANCCOB received no fewer than 4 214 oiled penguins, 90 per cent of them from the south coast. Most oiling incidents occur during winter storms between the months of July and September, in the latter part of the main breeding season when many adults are feeding large chicks and have to travel far to find sufficient food.

On 20 June 1994, a far greater disaster than the *Kapodistrias* oil spill threatened when the bulk ore carrier *Apollo Sea* broke up hours after setting sail from Saldanha Bay and sank near Dassen Island. Over 10 000 penguins were oiled. Most of these were captured and taken to the SANCCOB rescue centre and, although 50 per cent of them died in captivity, 5 213 were successfully cleaned and returned to the wild.

Of these, 4 076 penguins were marked with numbered flipper bands and at least 68 per cent were still alive one month after release. Of those known to have survived the first month, 84 per cent were still alive two to three years later.

Lightning can and does strike in the same place more than once. In May 1998, 150 tonnes of oil spilled into Cape Town harbour. Among the 500 oiled penguins taken to SANCCOB, 3 were survivors of the *Apollo Sea* spill four years before.

Among the 10 000 victims of the *Apollo Sea* spill at Dassen Island were 215 birds that had already been banded. Although the majority of them were local birds, some had been banded at localities as far away as Ichaboe Island, Namibia, and Bird Island, Algoa Bay. After the banding and release of survivors, at least 11 made it north to Ichaboe and 2 to Algoa's St Croix Island.

These observations suggest that penguins move around the coast far more than scientists had thought likely. The release of rehabilitated birds has also shown just how accurately and quickly they can find their way home: of the oiled birds transported from St Croix Island to Cape Town, where they were released, the first were back home in 11 days. To reach St Croix in such a short time, they had to travel an average of 81 km per day – helped, however, by a 23-km/h east-flowing current.

The rescue following the *Apollo Sea* disaster stretched SANCCOB's resources and its resourcefulness to untested limits, but worse was to come. On 23 June 2000, the bulk ore carrier *Treasure* sank off Robben Island (see pages 52–53), precipitating the largest seabird rescue mission the world has ever seen, larger even than those following the *Torrey Canyon* (off the southwest English coastline) and the *Exxon Valdez* (Alaska) disasters.

August 1983. Burning oil from the *Castillo de Bellver* on the Cape west coast between Saldanha and Cape Town. Unseasonal offshore winds prevented a catastrophe of spectacular proportions.

SURVIVAL OF REHABILITATED PENGUINS

The success and importance of SANCCOB's rehabilitation efforts were demonstrated recently by a study that analyzed the difference in the mortality rates of flipper-banded penguins, comparing birds that had not been oiled with ones that had been oiled, cleaned and subsequently released. The study clearly showed that there was no difference in the death rates of the two groups.

Not only do rehabilitated birds survive well, but they also breed successfully – some of them are among the oldest African Penguins known to be alive today. Indeed, the two oldest known African Penguins of all time are both birds that survived oiling and rehabilitation. One died at the age of 24; the other was last sighted alive and well at the same age.

Rehabilitation of oiled penguins has been more successful than that of other seabird species but, if oil spills continue at the present rate (since April 1968 there have been 14 significant oil spills off the Cape coast), the remaining penguin population will be unable to replace its losses.

SANCCOB can be contacted at P O Box 11116, Bloubergrant, 7443. Tel: (27 21) 557 6155. Fax: (27 21) 557 8804. E-mail: *sanccob@netactive.co.za*

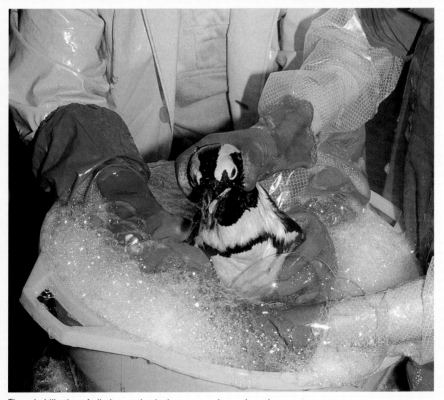

The rehabilitation of oiled penguins is time-consuming and costly.

Oiled adults

Captured chicks

Transport by road, sea and air

Holding cages for treatment

Recovery area

Hand-feeding the 20 000 oiled birds

Signs of hope

THE DRAMA OF THE TREASURE

Early in the morning of 23 June 2000 the bulk oil carrier *MV Treasure* foundered and sank in the ocean between Robben and Dassen islands, a few kilometres outside Cape Town harbour:

- More than 1 100 tonnes of heavy oil and 100 tonnes of lighter fuel oil spill into the sea.
- Next day, the first oiled penguins arrive on the two islands. During the night the booms erected to protect Robben Island are breached, and oil pollutes the island's rocky shores.
- On 28 June the slick reaches Dassen Island and large quantities of oil foul the coastline. Currents force the oil north, towards the shores of the West Coast National Park.
- Rescue efforts start immediately. Oiled penguins are removed from the islands, unoiled ones from the wider danger zone. Boats, trucks, helicopters and cargo aircraft are used to remove stricken birds – 14 825 from Robben Island, 3 516 from Dassen Island and a further 500 from elsewhere, including 194 from the national park, in what will go on record as the world's most massive rescue operation of its kind. An additional 3 350 chicks that would otherwise have starved to death are collected for hand-rearing.
- A total of 19 506 unoiled birds are captured from the two islands and taken 800 km by road to Cape Recife, near Port Elizabeth, well outside the danger zone, where there is plenty of food for them. They are then released to make their way back to their nesting sites – a journey likely to take at least 10 days, just enough time to clean up the oil.
- Hundreds of volunteers gather at SANCCOB's rehabilitation centre near Cape Town to wash and care for 19 000 oiled penguins. Their success is unprecedented in the annals of seabird rescues, but the disruption of pairing and breeding and moulting cycles will be felt for many years to come.

STATISTICAL SUMMARY

- About 20 000 adult and immature penguins are oiled along almost 150 km of coast: 1 700 die in captivity; fewer than 200 are thought to have died in the wild.
- 10% of the 3 350 captured chicks die; about 4 000 chicks starve to death on the two islands.
- 19 000-plus unoiled birds are transported to Cape Recife for release: 213 die on the way, and 30 at the release site; the survivors take 2–3 weeks to return home.
- In total, about 2 000 adult birds and 4 350 chicks perish as a result of the spill.

Release point at Cape Town . . .

. . . and freedom for the survivors.

NATURAL THREATS: PENGUINS' ENEMIES

Although African Penguins may not appeal to the human palate, some predators are quite happy to make a meal of them. They are certainly on the menu of sharks. In Algoa Bay, the Great White Shark *Carcharion carcharias* ranks second only to oil spills in killing African Penguins. Killer Whales also occasionally kill penguins, but probably not in significant numbers. However, penguins are very much aware of the risk, and when Killer Whale vocalisations are played underwater, the birds immediately flee the area. This behaviour has proved useful to conservationists. If underwater blasting is due to take place, for example, the penguins can be chased away from the danger area by playing tapes of Killer Whale calls.

The number of Cape Fur Seals *Arctocephalus pusillus* has increased dramatically around southern Africa in the past hundred years; the species' status has progressed from endangered to common. Some seals have become experts at catching and killing penguins. But, like the early explorers, they seem to dislike the flesh. Their interest lies in the birds' stomachs and the fish they contain.

Around Dyer Island, which is very close to a large seal colony, seals kill about 1 000 penguins each year. On Dassen Island, one seal alone was estimated to kill about 25 penguins a day. Like African Penguins, seals favour offshore islands as breeding sites and, once they have selected a site for a colony, the penguins are either forced to leave or prevented from colonizing. This has caused some concern, especially on Namibian islands where penguin numbers are in rapid decline.

Until the mid-1950s, penguins on Sinclair Island, Namibia, were protected from invasion by a

This victim of a shark attack is unlikely to survive its next trip to sea.

seal-proof wall, but when this was breached, many penguins were rapidly ousted and forced to relocate themselves on Plumpudding Island, about 2,5 km away. Some seal-scaring measures have been put in place at Mercury Island in an attempt to ensure that the penguins are allowed to continue breeding there.

Adult penguins are better equipped to escape predators in the sea than they are on land, which may be one reason why the majority of penguin colonies are sited on predator-free islands. At one island colony in Saldanha Bay, where construction of a breakwater between island and mainland allowed predators access, Large-spotted Genets *Genetta tigrina* killed several adult birds over a period of more than a year.

The small mainland colony at Betty's Bay was subject to the attentions of an even more powerful terrestrial predator: in just two nights in 1985, a single Leopard *Panthera pardus* killed at least 65 adult African Penguins (see page 63).

Some Cape Fur Seals are specialists at killing penguins.

Exposed eggs and small chicks are vulnerable to predators, especially opportunistic Kelp Gulls and Sacred Ibises. They are also killed by predators introduced by man, such as the domestic cat *Felis catus*, on Robben and Dassen islands. Before their numbers were reduced on Dassen in the mid 1980s, cats were estimated to kill 500 young penguins annually – about 10 per cent of all chicks born on the island. Mole Snakes *Pseudapsis cana* prey on penguin eggs and chicks on Robben Island. This may be a natural form of predation, as records of Mole Snakes on Robben Island date back to 1612, a time when introduction by man was unlikely.

Killer Whales wait at the seaward edge of the kelp bed to ambush unsuspecting prey.

Breeding in colonies does have certain advantages, but it also has drawbacks, including easy transmission of diseases and parasites. Penguins hatched in captivity are particularly susceptible to infestations of parasitic worms, but even in the wild these can cause problems and have led to the death of many chicks on islands in Algoa Bay. Diseases known to affect, and kill, penguins include avian malaria, avian cholera, babesia and Newcastle disease.

Generally, however, disease is more of a problem for penguins in captivity than for those in the wild. In the case of avian malaria, in particular, some concern has been expressed about the dangers of introducing the disease into wild populations when rehabilitated birds are released.

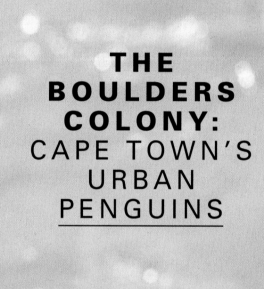

THE
BOULDERS
COLONY:
CAPE TOWN'S
URBAN
PENGUINS

*'Their diving suits are so well tailored
that not an icy drop touches
tender skin in months at sea.'*
Mike Holmes, *Cry of the Jackass*, 1976.

A viewing platform at Boulders Beach offers visitors an unrivalled penguin-watching experience.

On the 17th of November, 1982, an extraordinary discovery was made at Stony Point, on the western Cape mainland. A pair of penguins was incubating eggs at Betty's Bay only 60 km from Cape Town. Could this be a new penguin colony in the making? Indeed it was, and by 1986, the colony had grown to 35 pairs.

Two years after this discovery, on the dunes below Simon's Town on the southern Cape Peninsula, a pair of African Penguins was found at a nest, though it contained no eggs. The likelihood of a second mainland colony so close to Cape Town seemed remote. In March 1985, however, the penguin pioneers at Boulders Beach laid their first clutch.

The meteoric growth of the Boulders colony has been a great surprise to researchers. From the first pair in 1985, numbers have increased on average by

It seems incongruous that a vulnerable seabird should be thriving on the fringes of suburbia.

more than 60 per cent per year. By 1997, there were 2 350 adult birds in the colony – more than one per cent of the entire African Penguin population!

A likely reason for the success of the Boulders colony is that prime feeding conditions are available nearby, in False Bay. As early as 1966, it was officially recommended that commercial purse seine fishing be banned in the Bay, a ban that was implemented in 1984. Only in very recent years has a small number of pilchard fishermen been granted limited access to the inshore waters.

However, the proximity of good feeding grounds and high breeding success could not possibly account for the extent of the growth of the Boulders colony: the maximum growth rate that could be achieved by reproduction alone is barely 10 per cent per year. The only other way the colony could grow is by immigration, which is what appears to have happened.

Rehabilitated birds from SANCCOB have been seen at Boulders, and other individuals have come from as far away as Ichaboe and Mercury islands to the north, and from Bird Island, in Algoa Bay, to the east. Many of these appear to be itinerant birds, and only birds ringed at Dassen, Robben and Dyer islands are

WARNING

PENGUINS ON PARKING AREA

CHECK UNDER YOUR VEHICLE BEFORE DEPARTING

Coastal signage at Boulders.

known to have moved to Boulders to breed. The main source of Boulders' penguins is almost certainly Dyer Island, 105 km to the southeast. During the time the Boulders colony has been expanding, the numbers on Dyer Island have crashed.

There is one other African Penguin colony in False Bay – on Seal Island 20 km to the east. In the 19th Century, as many as 5 000 pairs bred on this small rock outcrop. In modern times, however, it has been taken over by Cape Fur Seals and only about 100 penguin pairs still manage to find space to breed there. It is unlikely, therefore, that Seal Island has been a significant supplier of birds to Boulders.

The breeding colony at Boulders is still fairly small, covering roughly two hectares. Relative to some other colonies, nests at Boulders are not particularly close together: their density averages

Look left, look right . . . urban penguins on the move!

A group of penguins returns to Boulders Beach after a hunt in False Bay.

A rare visitor to Boulders, a Greater Sheathbill *Chionis alba* from Antarctica forages among the penguins (September 2000).

to expand. It is difficult to guess its eventual size, but a figure has been suggested of around 2 500 pairs.

In the colony's early days, Simon's Town residents were very protective of their feathered lodgers. As numbers grew, however, so did noise, smell and damage to gardens, and attitudes started to change! In December 1996, a chain-link fence was erected along Willis Walk. This has successfully confined the colony to the area below the fence, where there is still plenty of room.

An unusual sight at any colony – a melanistic penguin comes ashore at Boulders.

about 300 nests per hectare. This contrasts with St Croix Island, where nests are packed together at densities of up to 1 600 per hectare.

Although the growth in numbers at Boulders seems to be slowing down, scientists agree that, provided no catastrophe occurs, the colony will continue

THREATS TO THE BOULDERS COLONY

The African Penguins at Boulders are extraordinarily tame and are accustomed to humans. However, because they are breeding on the mainland, they face threats that are absent or minimal on islands. Predators have ready access to the colony, and feral dogs and cats, as well as genets, take their toll. Of these, genets are probably the most serious threat. In 1997 alone, more than 70 recently-fledged chicks were killed. Most, if not all, of these killings were thought to be the work of genets.

Avian malaria is generally not a problem on islands because the land birds that carry the disease, and the mosquitoes that transmit it, are absent. Several malaria-carrying land-bird species do, however, occur around Boulders, placing at risk the penguins, who have a very low natural resistance to the disease.

Oil pollution is an ever-present threat and so, at Boulders, is fire. The natural plant life of the Cape Peninsula is mountain fynbos, a type of vegetation that is entirely dependent on periodic fire for regeneration. The penguins' breeding area is also covered with alien plant species imported from fire-prone areas.

A fire out of control at Boulders could have consequences frightening to contemplate. Robben Island, which is also heavily covered with alien vegetation, faces the same threat.

Fire ravages the mountainside above Simon's Town (January 2000).

ROBBEN ISLAND: ANOTHER SUCCESS STORY

There are records of African Penguins breeding on Robben Island as early as 1620. However, the island was readily accessible to the early colonists of the Cape, and by the late 18th Century the penguin population had been hunted to extinction. The African Penguin was to remain extinct as a breeding species on Robben Island for the next two hundred years.

Then, in 1983 (some ten years before the notorious prison closed its doors for the last time), 18 breeding African Penguins were found on Robben Island. This population has since risen to about 15 000 birds, including 5 700 breeding pairs.

As at Boulders, this rate of growth can be explained only by immigration; the birth rate accounts for only about 40 per cent of the increase. Of the immigrants, more than 60 per cent have come from Dyer Island, 165 km to the southeast; the remainder from Dassen Island, 50 km to the north. Numbers have been falling rapidly at Dyer Island since the mid-1980s, owing mainly to a shortage of food, and many penguins have found new homes with a prime view of Table Mountain.

Robben Island is also regularly used as a release site for penguins that have been rehabilitated at SANCCOB. Over 1 000 were released here in 1972, and more than 1 500 in 1984 and 1985. Few of these have remained to breed, but their mere presence may have stimulated young birds, perhaps pairs breeding for the first time, to take up residence and start a colony. There is no shortage of suitable, shady breeding habitat for those that do, and there are ample food supplies nearby.

Despite the numbers of tourists visiting Robben Island, the colony continues to thrive and grow.

In 1983, African Penguins began to recolonize Robben Island after an absence of two hundred years.

THE OTHER MAINLAND COLONIES

STONY POINT

The African Penguin colony at Stony Point, adjacent to the village of Betty's Bay, started three years before the Boulders colony. However, its growth has not been nearly as dramatic, and predators have played a key role in keeping numbers down. When the colony had grown to 35 pairs in 1986, a lone Leopard *Panthera pardus* killed at least 65 penguins in just two nights, setting the colony back almost to square one.

By 1990, the colony had recovered and numbered 139 pairs, but in the following three years numbers decreased by more than 50 per cent to only 57 pairs. The decrease was due mainly to predation by another leopard – the first having been illegally shot by an overzealous landowner.

The other penguin predator at Stony Point is the Water Mongoose *Atilax paludinosus*. These animals were trapped and translocated, leading to a recovery in the number of penguins to about 130 pairs by 1996. Immigration from Dyer Island accounts for a large part of this recovery.

Growth of the Stony Point colony has been slowed by predatory leopards.

SYLVIA HILL

On the Namibian mainland between Mercury Island and Hollams Bird Island is the unique Sylvia Hill penguin colony. The birds breed in two large caves, 400 m apart – the only known cave-breeding African Penguins. Both caves are about 30 m deep; their entrances are partly submerged, and they are further protected from predators by rocks and pounding waves.

The colony of 40 birds (and six nests with eggs) was discovered in June 1980. How long it had remained undetected, no one knows. Since its discovery, 200 or more adults have been counted there at one time, but it seems as though breeding numbers are fairly stable at 20–30 pairs.

It is likely that other colonies of cave-breeding penguins are undiscovered on the Namibian coast. In March 1984, penguins were found in a cave 20 km south of Sylvia Hill and, another kilometre south, penguins were seen swimming into a gully at the base of sheer cliffs. Because the sites were so inacessible, researchers could not establish whether the birds were nesting in the caves.

Even the Black-backed Jackal *Canis mesomelas* cannot enter Sylvia Hill's caves.

THE COLONIAL MIX

'Beauty is lent to Penguin Island by the thousands of birds with whom the penguins share it as a home.'

Cherry Kearton, *Penguin Island,* 1960.

White-breasted Cormorant

Penguin colonies are often in close proximity to, or are even scattered between, the breeding colonies of other seabirds. Visitors to penguin areas should keep their eyes open for the following:

WHITE-BREASTED CORMORANT
Phalacrocorax carbo
This is southern Africa's largest marine cormorant. It usually breeds on tall rocks with good all-round visibility. The white fore-neck and breast make this bird unmistakable. (Alternative name: Great Cormorant)

BANK CORMORANT
Phalacrocorax neglectus
Red Data Book Species. The population is decreasing rapidly because of competition for space with seals and, among other things, disturbance by man. This is a large, all-dark cormorant with a black bill, bronze and turquoise eye and no brightly coloured skin at the base of the bill. When they are breeding, adults have a white rump; no other local cormorant has this feature. The species is found only in southern Africa, almost exclusively on

Bank Cormorant

the west coast, where kelp is common. The Bank Cormorant is also unusual among local cormorants in that its nest is made up mostly of marine algae, which the birds collect live from the sea floor.

CAPE CORMORANT
Phalacrocorax capensis
This is the commonest local cormorant and is frequently seen flying low over the water in long, straggly lines. It sometimes feeds in flocks that number tens of thousands. It is all-dark like the Bank Cormorant, but has bright yellow skin at the base of the bill, and a brilliant, piercing turquoise eye. Breeds only in southern Africa.

Cape Cormorant

CROWNED CORMORANT
Phalacrocorax coronatus
Red Data Book Species. This is by far the smallest of the four marine cormorants and is proportionally longer tailed than the other species. It has a red eye, reddish-orange skin around the face and throat and a small, pointed tuft of feathers

Crowned Cormorant

at the base of the bill (hence its common name). It often breeds lower down on rocks than the other cormorants, frequently in cracks and fissures. Also breeds in bushes. Found only in southern Africa, mostly on the west coast.

CAPE GANNET
Morus capensis
This is a large, predominantly white seabird with black on the wings and tail, often seen flying offshore, frequently in flocks. Groups perform spectacular diving displays when feeding on shoals of fish

67

Cape Gannet

near the tip; the legs and the feet are greenish-grey. The bird is common along the southern African coastline and readily gathers to feed at fish factories and rubbish dumps. The young bird (seen in the foreground of the photo) is dark-billed and mottled brownish-black all over, becoming progressively more black and white as it grows older. (Alternative name: Southern Black-backed Gull)

HARTLAUB'S GULL
Larus hartlaubii
A common gull of the west and south-west coasts, endemic to southern Africa. Predominantly white, with dark-tipped, pale grey wings and a pale grey back. The bill and legs are deep red, sometimes appearing black. Usually found in flocks, often at coastal picnic sites.

Hartlaub's Gull

that are driven to the surface in an effort to escape from larger, predatory fish. Young birds progress from a mottled brown to white.

KELP GULL
Larus dominicanus
A large gull, with white head, neck and underparts and black upper wings and back. The bill is yellow with a red mark

Kelp Gull

SWIFT TERN
Sterna bergii
Many species of tern occur along the southern African coast, especially during the summer months between November and March. The Swift Tern is easily identified by its large size (slightly larger than the Hartlaub's Gull) and its dagger-like yellow bill. In breeding plumage it has a

jet-black crown and crest; outside the breeding period, the black marking is largely confined to the hind crown. (Alternative name: Greater Crested Tern)

Swift Tern

AFRICAN BLACK OYSTERCATCHER
Haematopus moquini
Red Data Book Species. World population about 5 000 birds (1 600 breeding pairs). This large, black shorebird is quite unmistakable with its long red bill, pink legs, red eye and orange eye-ring. Usually seen in pairs, except at high tide when it forms communal roosts. Found only in southern Africa, with about 75 per cent of the entire population in South Africa.

African Black Oystercatcher

RUDDY TURNSTONE
Arenaria interpres
Many species of migratory shorebirds that breed at the edge of the Arctic migrate south to southern Africa for the warm summer months. Ruddy Turnstones are often seen busily foraging on rocky shores or along weed-strewn driftlines. They are easily identified by their short, stubby bills, short orange legs and strongly mottled upper parts.

Ruddy Turnstone

CAPE WAGTAIL
Motacilla capensis
Although not, strictly speaking, shorebirds, Cape Wagtails often forage along the shore. They are small, predominantly grey-brown birds with long grey tails that they wag up and down conspicuously as they move along.

Cape Wagtail

69

'*Here is the earth. Don't spend it all at once.*'

Barty Philips

INDEX